D1203601

PROFESSOR CLARK

THE SCIENCE SHARK®

PRESENTS:

THE ARTS AND
SCIENCES OF
THE OCEANS

WWW.PROFESSORCLARKTHESCIENCESHARK.COM

PROFESSOR CLARK THE SCIENCE SHARK Book 2 ***"Going Home"***
™Trademark Reg. No. 4,450,531
Copyright © 2014 by Scott and Karen Lamberson.
All rights reserved.

Published by Professor Clark the Science Shark
2433 Hope Lane
Palm Beach Gardens, FL 33410
www.ProfessorClarktheScienceShark.com

Book layout by SuOakes Graphic Design, Lake Worth, FL
www.suoakesdesign.com

Printed in the United States of America
ISBN: 978-1-5136-0566-1

Book 2, **Going Home** is dedicated
to all the lovers of the sea, to the
sea's incredible inhabitants, and to
the next generation of children!

Make sure you visit us at our educational
website and on social media!

www.ProfessorClarktheScienceShark.com

Instagram: @professorclarkthescienceshark

Facebook: https://www.facebook.com/ProfessorClark

It's Professor Clark the Science Shark, and I'd like to include you on another aquatic journey as I tell the story of my life in "Going Home". It was in this chapter of my life that I realized who I was and why I have such a big responsibility to educate the next generation.

Well, my friends, the sharks and coral reefs are in the news a lot these days, and I've been called in to help educate all of the humans on the important role that sharks, like me, play in maintaining our oceans and beautiful coral reefs.

CORAL REEFS are found throughout the world and are called "the rainforest of the oceans." They play such an important part in keeping our oceans vibrant with life. Sharks are needed to help keep the ecosystems of the oceans and reefs healthy and in balance. It's a pretty big job, and that's why I need help from you kids!

In the process of swimming through the passages of my life, I am hoping to gain more and more human friends just like you who don't fear me but respect me and my kind. Then maybe, just maybe, all of us can make a stand and join hands and fins to become **AMBASSADORS OF THE SEAS!**

Fincerely,

Professor Clark The Science Shark

Somewhere deep in the middle of the **ATLANTIC OCEAN**, a beautiful tiger shark named Clark was deep in thought as he reflected on his incredible journey that brought him there.

Clark closed his eyes and remembered **VIVIDLY** the details about that day. He remembered how hungry he was and how the sting from the shiny lure with the hidden hook caused him to immediately spit it out.

He could also never forget seeing
his first human – a little boy.
Clark gulped. The memories
of that day reminded him of
the pain and the fear, but also
the **FASCINATION** that he had
experienced in just a few brief
moments – moments that would
change Clark's life forever.

REMINISCING back to that day, Clark wasn't sure why he took off swimming after that encounter, as he ended up hundreds of miles away from home with his faithful friend, Ray the Remora. Together they found a new coral reef far away from any sign of land.

The time spent on a far away reef was actually very good for Clark. He grew in size and in wisdom about the oceans. In fact, he became quite the expert in all things that helped form the **ECOSYSTEMS** of the ocean. "A coral reef is created by layers of organisms called **POLYPS**", a beaming Professor Clark told Ray. Ray was so impressed by Clark's newfound **KNOWLEDGE** that he gave the **EXTRAORDINARY** tiger shark a new name!

"Professor Clark the Science Shark,"
Ray exclaimed, "YOU ARE AWESOME!"

Clark finished thinking about those memories from long ago as he poked his head above the water and let out a big sigh. "Do you ever think about what goes on in our ocean, Ray?" Professor Clark asked with a certain heaviness in his voice.

Without saying more, the now mature
tiger shark swam quickly to the
bottom of the ocean floor.

"When I look around, I see beauty, but I also see problems. I see changes in the reefs and in the water. I have to do something about it, Ray!" Clark proclaimed with **DETERMINATION**.

Ray did not fully understand the depth of Clark's concern, but he knew if anyone was equipped to handle the **COMPLEX** problems in the ocean, it would be Professor Clark the Science Shark.

Even the sea creatures knew about the tiger shark with the amazing knowledge of their waters and reefs.

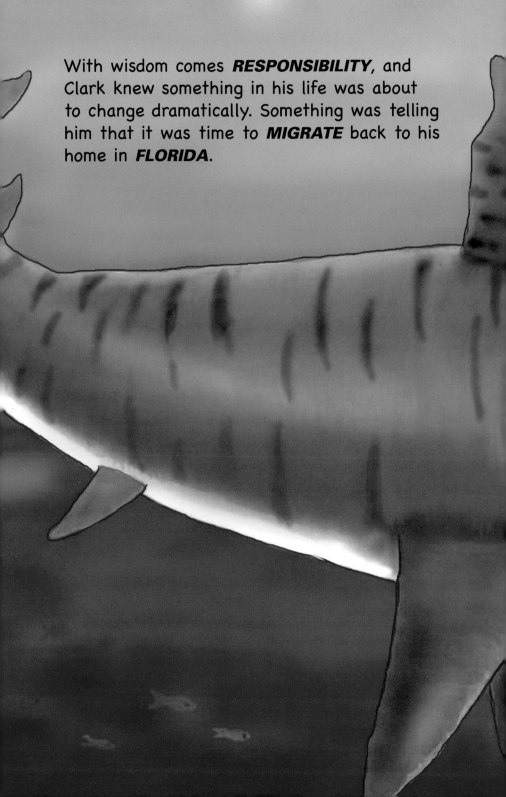

With wisdom comes **RESPONSIBILITY**, and Clark knew something in his life was about to change dramatically. Something was telling him that it was time to **MIGRATE** back to his home in **FLORIDA**.

With sadness, Professor Clark told his friends about his decision to leave the reef that had taught him so much about life. Ray did not know what to say, but he knew that he would follow his friend Clark wherever his journeys would take him.

Very early the next morning, the two friends began their long journey back to their home off the east coast of Jupiter, Florida. As they swam, Clark explained to Ray about the day he would never forget – the day he almost swallowed a hook and met a little boy, his first and only human encounter.

Clark showed Ray the place on his lip
where he felt the sting of the hook.
"I haven't forgotten that boy, and
I don't know why," Clark whispered
softly as they swam on.

Clark and Ray were both very
happy when they finally arrived
back on Clark's familiar reef.

His happiness soon turned to grief, however, when he looked at the once *PRISTINE* coral that was now covered in green and brown *ALGAE*! "What happened to our beautiful coral reef?" Professor Clark cried out in dismay. Suddenly, he understood.

There was a reason why he felt something telling him to return home, and Clark somehow knew this was just the beginning. The oceans' ecosystems were in trouble, and he, Professor Clark, would need to educate the world! But how? With whom?

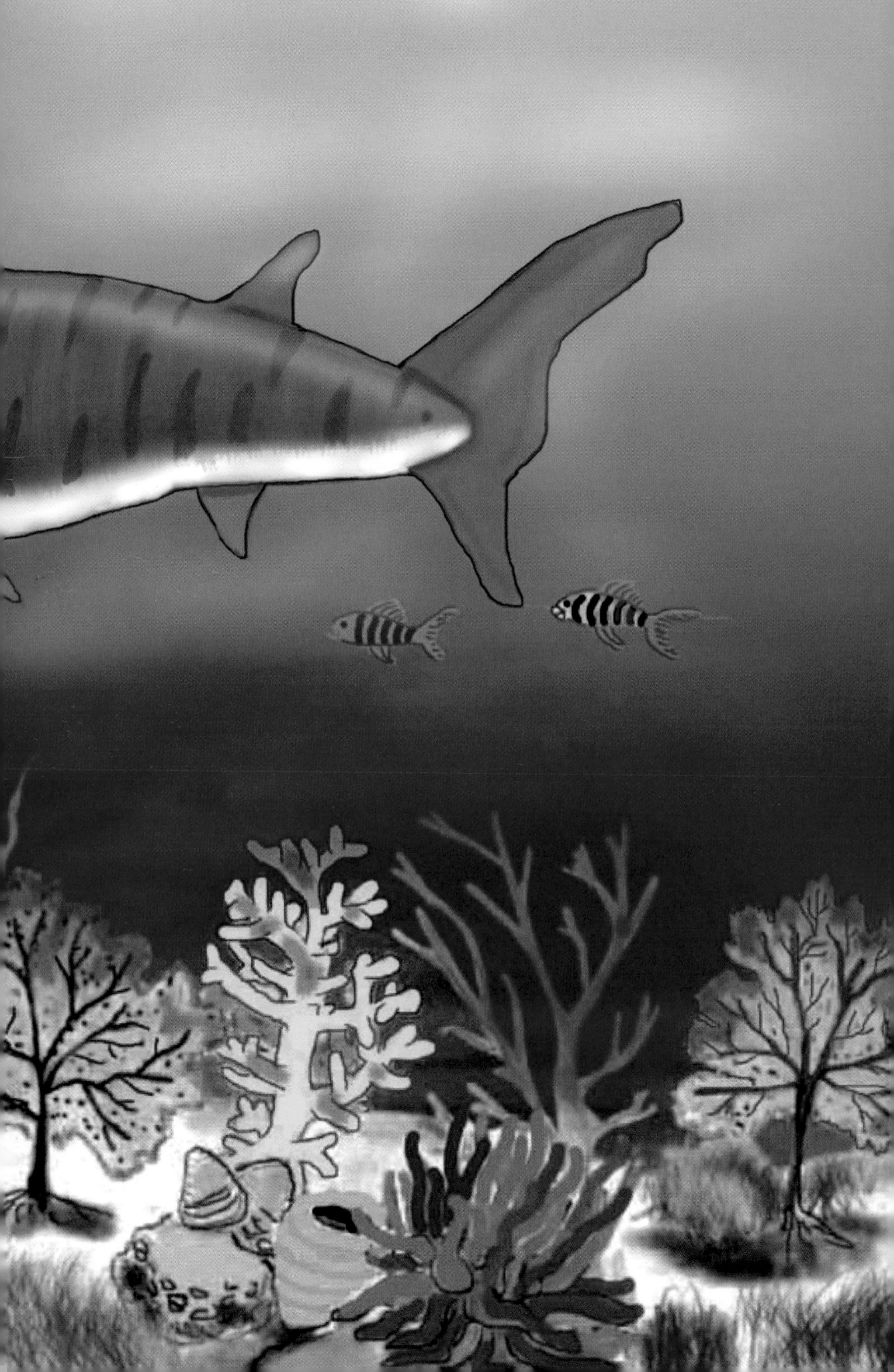

43

TO BE CONTINUED ...

PROFESSOR CLARK THE SCIENCE SHARK'S VOCAB LAB

CORAL REEFS: underwater structures constructed by tiny animals called coral. They are the most beautiful yet fragile ecosystems in the world. Approximately one fourth of all marine life depends on coral reefs for survival. We must do all we can to protect our coral reefs.

ATLANTIC OCEAN: the world's second largest ocean located between North America and Europe/Africa.

VIVIDLY: strikingly bright or intense, forming distinct and striking mental images.

FASCINATION: the state of being intensely interested or attracted.

REMINISCING: to think back or tell of past experiences or events.

ECOSYSTEMS: biological environments consisting of all the organisms living in a particular area, as well as the physical components of the environment with which the organisms interact, such as air, soil, water and sunlight.

POLYP: an invertebrate animal (sea anemone or coral) having a hollow cylinder-shaped body closed and attached at one end and opening at the other by a central mouth surrounded by tentacles armed with minute stinging organs.

KNOWLEDGE: familiarity, awareness, or understanding gained through experience or study.

EXTRAORDINARY: exceptional in character, amount, extent, degree, etc.; noteworthy; remarkable.

DETERMINATION: firmness of purpose, will or intention.

COMPLEX: composed of many interconnected parts.

RESPONSIBILITY: taking care of your duties and answering for your actions. Responsibility is accountability and trustworthiness.

MIGRATE: the periodic passage of a group of animals (especially birds or fishes) from one region to another for feeding or breeding.

FLORIDA: a peninsular state in southeastern United States which has the Atlantic Ocean and Gulf of Mexico surrounding most of its coast.

PRISTINE: remaining in a pure state; uncorrupted by civilization. Remaining free from dirt or decay; clean.

ALGAE: a large and diverse group of simple organisms ranging from unicellular to multicellular forms. The largest and most complex marine forms are commonly known as seaweeds.

Professor Clark's Fun Fin Facts

▶ Ocean

The ocean is a body of salt water that covers more than seventy percent of the earth's surface. Ninety-seven percent of the earth's water is in the ocean. The Atlantic Ocean has the most salt content. The Arctic Ocean has the least salt content. The earth's oceans are all connected.

Research: Why do the earth's oceans have different salt contents?

▶ Life Cycle of a Coral Reef

Some coral reefs began growing on the planet 50 million years ago. Their life cycles are unlimited. Although coral reefs cover only .1% of the ocean floors, they support approximately 25% of all marine creatures. Healthy reefs can grow up to 3 centimeters wide and 25 centimeters tall per year.

Research: What can humans do to reduce the threat to coral reefs?

▶ Habitat

A habitat is the place where a species lives. It is the place that provides everything the species needs to survive, including, food, water, and space to grow.

Research: What is the natural habitat for Professor Clark the Science Shark?

▶ Algae

Corals have a delicate relationship with algae. Algae live inside the corals, and the algae help corals get food and oxygen. However, too much algae can kill the coral. Pollution from local waterways can cause overgrowth of algae. Over-fishing also contributes to overgrowth of algae, as overfishing removes the fish from the reef. The fish eat the algae to keep it from taking over the reef.

Research: What is the most common type of algae found in the coral reef?

Swimming through Standards

SC.4.N.2.1 - Explain that science focuses solely on the natural world.

SC.4.L.17.4 - Recognize ways plants and animals, including humans, can impact the environment.

SC.2.L.17.2 - Recognize and explain that living things are found all over Earth, but each is only able to live in habitats that meet its basic needs.

SC.1.E.6.1 - Recognize that water, rocks, soil, and living organisms are found on Earth's surface.

SC.1.L.14.1 - Make observations of living things and their environment using the five senses.

SC.1.L.17.1 Through observation, recognize that all plants and animals, including humans, need the basic necessities of air, water, food, and space.

SC.K.N.1.5 - Recognize that learning can come from careful observation.

SC.K.L.14.2 - Recognize that some books and other media portray animals and plants with characteristics and behaviors they do not have in real life.

Andrew "Red" Harris Foundation

Gulfstream currents bring the life that is settling on our modules and the adjacent re-exposed bedrock and interact with them to scour away the smothering sand that has been preventing growth on

the underlying bedrock. More than 75 kinds of fish swarm on the reef, turtles visit to rest and use the reef as a cleaning station, dozens of sea plant species are growing and corals are already returning. The Foundation donated 15 lagoon size coral head replica modules to the renowned Blue Heron Bridge snorkeling trail. Our intricate reef structures serve as beautiful guideposts that allow everyone to experience the foundation's beautiful "Lagoon Coral Head" modules first hand in a lifeguarded county park.

http://AndrewRedHarrisFoundation.org 18230 River Oaks Dr., Jupiter, Fl 33458